David McFetrich first qualified as a civil engineer and his work included acting as project manager in the construction of three bridges. He then joined an international management consultancy firm, undertaking assignments in many parts of the world, and is now an independent business consultant.

Jo Parsons has had a lifelong interest in photography. After achieving the City & Guilds certificate and gaining her L.R.P.S. she has enjoyed success in competitions and has exhibited locally.

Following page
Town Bridge, Christchurch.

DISCOVER DORSET

BRIDGES

DAVID McFETRICH AND
JO PARSONS

THE DOVECOTE PRESS

An engraving of one of Dorset's many small and attractive
eighteenth century bridges, Kingstag Bridge over the River
Lydden in the heart of the Blackmore Vale.

First published in 1998 by The Dovecote Press Ltd
Stanbridge, Wimborne, Dorset BH21 4JD

ISBN 1 874336 51 2

Text © David McFetrich 1998
Illustrations © Jo Parsons 1998

David McFetrich and Jo Parsons have asserted their rights
under the Copyright, Designs and Patent Act 1988
to be identified as authors of this work

Series designed by Humphrey Stone

Typeset in Sabon by The Typesetting Bureau
Wimborne, Dorset
Printed and bound by Baskerville Press, Salisbury, Wiltshire

A CIP catalogue record for this book is available
from the British Library

1 3 5 7 9 8 6 4 2

CONTENTS

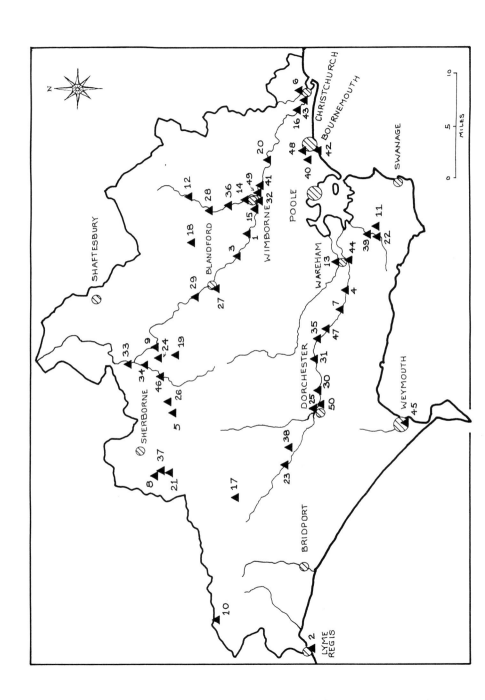

DORSET BRIDGES

No	Name	Location	Date	Map Ref
Medieval & 16th Century				
1	White Mill	Sturminster Marshall	1175	957 005
2	Buddle	Lyme Regis		342 921
3	Crawford	Spettisbury		919 020
4	Holme	Holmebridge		890 866
5	Cornford	Holwell	1480	691 120
6	Town	Christchurch		160 928
7	Old	Wool		844 871
8	Smith's	Bradford Abbas		589 140
9	Town	Sturminster Newton		784 135
10	Axe	Thorncombe		362 053
11	Outer	Corfe Castle		959 822
12	Stanbridge Mill	Horton		014 088
17th Century				
13	North	Wareham		921 878
14	Walford	Wimborne		009 006
15	Julian's	Wimborne	1636	003 998
16	Iford	Christchurch		136 935
17	Packhorse	Rampisham		562 023
18	Packhorse	Tarrant Monkton		945 091
19	Packhorse	Fifehead Neville		711 111
18th Century				
20	Longham	Hampreston	1728	064 973
21	Beer Hackett	Beer Hackett		590 125
22	Vineyard	Corfe Castle		957 822
23	Court	Frampton		632 946
24	Rolls Mill	Sturminster Newton		884 133
25	Grey's	Dorchester	1748	700 908
26	Higher Wood	Bishop's Caundle	1770	707 126
27	Blandford	Blandford	1783	883 060
28	Witchampton	Witchampton	1795	990 061
29	Durweston	Durweston	1795	863 086
19th Century				
30	Lower Bockhampton	Stinsford		721 907
31	Frome	Tincleton		769 909
32	Canford	Wimborne	1813	016 922
33	King's Mill	Marnhull	1823	767 170
34	Bagber	Bagber	1830	764 157
35	Hurst South	Moreton	1834	769 909
36	Fitches	Pamphill	1841	006 025
37	Longford	Thornford		590 130
38	Frampton Viaduct	Sydling St Nicholas	1857	640 945
39	Railway Viaduct	Corfe Castle	1885	960 824
40	Bourne Valley Viaduct	Poole	1885	062 924
41	Suspension	Canford Magna		030 988
20th Century				
42	Alum Chine	Bournemouth	1904	071 905
43	Tuckton	Bournemouth	1905	149 922
44	South	Wareham	1927	924 872
45	Town	Weymouth	1930	678 787
46	Twofords	Lydlinch	1942	751 137
47	Ford footbridge	Moreton	1950	806 895
48	Braidley Road	Bournemouth	1970	085 916
49	River Stour	Wimborne	1981	025 990
50	St George's Viaduct	Dorchester	1988	705 904

[7]

INTRODUCTION

Bridges are the oldest engineering works designed by man, symbolising his conquest of nature. Their antecedents go right back to the use of a fallen log to cross a stream - the first primitive beam bridge - or to someone struggling across a gorge on a web of hanging vegetation - the first suspension bridge. The development of bridges from these simple origins to today's highly complex structures represents a fascinating story of great technical achievement. However, the interest of bridges is not just in how they work but is also concerned with the human story of who first built them and why. Unfortunately, many of the answers to these social questions remain teasingly unfound.

The development of bridges underpins the history of England as the earlier fords and ferries were replaced by fixed river crossings. The original settlement in London, for example, marks the lowest point at which the river could be crossed, initially by ford and later by the construction of the series of bridges known as London Bridge. Similarly Dorset's ancient bridges, themselves often replacements of even earlier structures, mark key points in the historic communications network of the county.

The challenge of providing safe and economic crossings has been solved in a variety of ways. The first timber beam bridges go back into pre-history and the earliest known stone arch bridge dates from more than four thousand years ago, but the records are sketchy. In England, not a single bridge, of either wood or stone, is specifically mentioned in the Domesday survey of 1086. The oldest bridge in Dorset, White Mill Bridge at Sturminster Marshall, has its origins dating back to 1174, two years before Peter of Colechurch began work on the stone arches of Old London Bridge, but it is not clear whether it was a timber beam or stone arch structure.

The medieval Smith's Bridge, Bradford Abbas, over the River Yeo.

The layman can usually understand the basic mechanics of the bridge and can certainly appreciate the courage and dedication of the builders in beating the forces of nature. At first these builders were the designers and craftsmen who built the major sacred and secular buildings of the Middle Ages. Over the years this design role developed into that of the architect until, following the Industrial Revolution, new materials of cast and wrought iron and then steel were developed, and the specialist civil engineer emerged to handle the increasing technical complexities. But a well-designed bridge of any age remains essentially a balanced fusion between architectural sensitivities regarding form and line and the engineering skills of fitting structure to purpose.

Dorset's bridges reflect the nature of the county and its people. There are no huge estuaries to cross, no mighty ravines to span; the age of the canal passed the county by and, with no major manufacturing industries to serve, the railway age arrived late (in 1847); the age of the motorway has not yet arrived. Nevertheless, in its own quiet way, the county has contributed to the continuing saga of British bridges: its ancient bridges are an integral part of the peaceful scenery which has attracted travellers and tourists since their construction made such travel possible, and at different times in this century its modern bridges have been right at the forefront of technology.

An unusual feature on some of the Dorset bridges is the 'Transportation for Life' plates, which were fixed on them to deter vandals following an Act of Parliament passed in 1827. The relevant part of the Act reads:

'And be it enacted, That if any Person shall unlawfully and maliciously pull down or in anywise destroy any public Bridge, or do any Injury with Intent and so thereby to render such Bridge or any Part thereof dangerous or impassable, every such Offender shall be guilty of Felony, and, being convicted thereof, shall be liable, at the Discression of the Court, to be transported beyond the Seas for Life, or for any Term not less than Seven Years, or to be imprisoned for any Term not exceeding Four Years; and, if a Male, to be once, twice, or thrice publicly or privately whipped (if the Court shall so think fit), in addition to such Imprisonment.'

The 'Transportation for Life' plate on the Old Bridge, Wool.

Twenty bridges still have transportation plates attached. The records do not show whether transportation was ever enforced for damage to a bridge before it was abolished by the Penal Servitude Acts of 1853 and 1857.

This little book surveys some of the best surviving examples of the bridges built in Dorset over the last 800 years. As far as possible, the selection of bridges has been made to reflect the geographical, historical and technical diversity of Dorset's several thousand bridges, as well as to choose those that are the most photogenic. There is a short description of each of the 50 bridges included in this selection, covering its structure, approximate size, and the date of its completion (where known), together with a note on any other points of interest.

A few technical terms have been used, where these are more concise than a wordy general description, and a full explanation of them is given in the Glossary. The dimensions are indicative and are not necessarily totally accurate. They have been given in the Imperial units in which the older structures were built and metric units for those bridges constructed since the mid 1970s. The dates of the older bridges are often conjectural, with the various authorities sometimes differing by a century or two. In general, the bridges have been ordered by the probable date when the main structure, as it now appears, was first built. The Outer Bridge at Corfe Castle (11) is thus listed as a sixteenth century bridge, even though its north abutment is far older than this, and Cornford Bridge at Holwell (5) is listed as medieval, even though it was substantially rebuilt in the eighteenth century, but with the original shape and structure.

THE MIDDLE AGES AND
TUDOR PERIOD

In 1066 few, if any, stone bridges had been built anywhere in England since the heights of the Roman occupation about eight hundred years earlier. After the Conquest, however, there was a tremendous burst of building activity, initially of castles and cathedrals, and considerable skills were developed in constructing arches to span openings. At first these were the semicircular Romanesque arches typical of Norman buildings but, by the end of the twelfth century, the pointed or Gothic arch had begun to appear.

Under the Normans, the construction and maintenance of bridges was primarily the responsibility of the local inhabitants. But these duties were so frequently neglected that the Church began to encourage their being undertaken as acts of piety. This soon led to it using its power and building skills to repair and then to construct bridges directly, often funding the work by the sale of indulgences (forgiveness of sins). It was natural, therefore, that the ecclesiastical bridge builders would adopt the latest techniques used in their cathedrals, and pointed arch bridges began to appear.

Semicircular arches, although relatively easy to set out and construct and intrinsically very strong, can quickly become unstable if there should be any movement of the foundations. On the other hand, pointed arches exert less horizontal force on their foundations and remain structurally stable, although unsightly, even if their piers should move slightly. Early medieval bridges are thus typified by small span semicircular arches, such as at Sturminster Marshall (1), or narrow pointed arches, as at Holwell (5), spanning between massive piers protected against possible undermining from scour by pointed cutwaters. The size of the piers would enable the arches to be constructed one span at a time, thereby reducing the need for scarce skilled labour and temporary centering. Each arch would itself often be built like a stone roofed building, with a series of intermediate ribs constructed first, and the rest of the arch vault would then be built to span between these ribs.

Towards the end of this early period of English bridge building, activity declined as a result of the Dissolution of the Monasteries (1535-36) and Civil Wars. In those bridges that were built, spans lengthened and pier thicknesses were reduced. The structures themselves became lighter as the arches started to be shaped to the profile of a segment of a circle rather than a full semicircle, for example at Wool (7), and the Tudor four-centred arch was introduced, for example at Bradford Abbas (8).

There are probably fewer than twenty ancient bridges from this period still standing in Dorset, but all have been extensively rebuilt, and many of them widened, over the years.

I. WHITE MILL BRIDGE
STURMINSTER MARSHALL

No-one knows how old this bridge is, although it is generally considered to be the oldest and most beautiful in the county. A bridge over the Stour near White Mill was recorded in 1174-75 but it is not certain how much, if any, of the original bridge remains in the existing structure. However, the lower portions are probably twelfth century work, whilst the original arches may have been rebuilt in the sixteenth century.

The bridge is known to have undergone considerable repairs during its lifetime. For example, in 1341 a Richard Bryan left three shillings in his will for the repair of it and the bridges at Blandford and Wimborne. In 1667 the County took over responsibility for the bridge from the parish and ordered major repairs in 1713. In 1909 the roadway was lowered nine inches and relaid in reinforced concrete and in 1964 and 1965 the timber rafts, which support the piers on top of the oak piles, were replaced by concrete. Unusually for such an old bridge, it does not appear to have been widened,

White Mill Bridge, Sturminster Marshall.

although this may have been because its width of 12 ft between parapets would have been generous for a rural medieval bridge.

The bridge consists of eight semicircular stone arches, each with four ribs. The alternate white limestone and red sandstone voussoirs are clearly visible on the outer ribs and give the bridge its distinctive appearance. There are four central arches of about 20 ft span and two smaller outer ones at each end of about 16 ft span. Both the upstream and downstream ends of the piers are protected by massive cutwaters which rise up to the full height of the parapet walls to provide pedestrian refuges. Between cutwaters the parapet rests on a projecting horizontal string course supported by small corbels. The level of this string course rises as the outer arches increase in diameter towards the central four arches, and the parapet wall itself is built to give a long and attractive vertically curved profile.

White Mill Bridge features in a popular old Dorset legend in which the people of Sturminster Marshall, needing new bells for their church, took the bells from the ruined church at Knowlton but then, finding themselves being chased by Knowlton folk, decided to drop the bells into the river from the bridge. When the thieves returned later to fish out their loot, they were unable to stop the bells from slipping back under water every time they had them almost in their grasp. And, so the story goes, there the bewitched bells remain to this day.

2. BUDDLE BRIDGE, LYME REGIS

This bridge probably dates back to the early fourteenth century and consists of a single 18 ft span pointed and ribbed arch. Two of the original four ribs still exist, together with recent replacements for the other two. The bridge was widened on both sides in 1913 and can only be seen from underneath, approached from the beach.

Following the demolition of some dilapidated cottages on the seaward side during the widening of 1913 a stone arched recess was discovered. This may have been a priest's cell, whose occupant collected tolls and dues on salt for the Abbot of Sherborne from those crossing the bridge.

3. CRAWFORD BRIDGE, SPETISBURY

A bridge over the Stour has been recorded on this site since before 1235, when forty days of indulgence were granted to those who contributed to its repair, with Edith Coker, abbess of Tarrant Crawford Abbey, appointed to receive the gifts.

The present bridge probably dates from the fourteenth or fifteenth century. It was largely rebuilt in 1506 and further repaired in 1705 and 1719. In 1819, the downstream cutwaters were removed and the bridge was widened to 12 ft between parapets. The two faces of the bridge are therefore now very different, with the cutwaters on the north face giving the bridge a lively medieval elevation, whilst on the downstream side it is possible to see all the arches and the whole length of the bridge, including an unusual southward kink at the east end, from a little shingle beach by the west abutment.

The structure consists of nine nearly semicircular stone arches 12 ft to 20 ft in span, five of the arches being ribbed. Alternate upstream

Buddle Bridge, Lyme Regis.

cutwaters are extended up to produce four triangular pedestrian refuges.

In her book about the Stour, *Dorset River*, Monica Hutchins records the memoirs of Arthur Field, vicar of Spetisbury and Charlton Marshall in the early twentieth century, when eels were taken in large numbers from the hatches near the bridge for sale in Wimborne and Blandford. Arthur Field also recalls a friend catching two pike, one weighing 21 lbs, the other 19½, within an hour in a backwater below the bridge.

4. HOLME BRIDGE, HOLMEBRIDGE

This bridge is generally considered to date from the fifteenth century, although it is likely that there has been a bridge crossing the Piddle on this site since the thirteenth century. It consists of six spans of which three are the original semicircular stone arches, spanning 12 ft, 14 ft and 12 ft, supported by piers with upstream cutwaters, extended up to parapet level to provide pedestrian refuges. There is also a fourth segmental stone arch, probably built in 1674, an eighteenth century brick arch at the north end and a nineteenth century stone arch with brick spandrels at the south end. These later arches incorporate pedestrian refuges over brick cutwaters on stone foundations. The old parapets, which were damaged by tanks on training exercises during the Second World War, have been replaced with brick walls surmounted by stone copings.

In 1643, during the Civil War, there was a skirmish on the bridge between a small group from the Royalist garrison at Wareham and 300 'rebels'. The captain and lieutenant of the garrison force, both having been wounded, ordered their troops to lay them on the edge of the bridge from where they continued to direct their men until a relieving party arrived and chased off the enemy. Forty of the rebels were killed and the lieutenant bled to death, 'encouraging his men with great cheerfulness.'

Opposite page top Crawford Bridge, Spetisbury.
Opposite page bottom Holme Bridge, Holmebridge.

5 . CORNFORD BRIDGE, HOLWELL

This attractive narrow bridge over Caundle Brook is called after the field name closest to the bridge. It has been dated to around 1480, although it was extensively repaired in the eighteenth century, and consists of three pointed stone arches spanning about 11 ft between massive piers.

For such a small bridge, it combines an number of interesting features. On the upstream face the two pointed cutwaters continue up to parapet level but have been partly capped off to leave very small refuges. On the downstream face the piers beneath the larger refuges are very different, the north pier ending with an ecclesiastical style buttress whilst the south pier has the normal pointed cutwater. The north abutment has clearly visible stepped foundations. In 1994 the bridge was the subject of a major repair, strengthening and cleaning project which was completed with great sympathy for the integrity of this scheduled ancient monument.

6. TOWN BRIDGE, CHRISTCHURCH

As with most medieval bridges, the original date of construction of this bridge over the River Avon is not known, but a record of its repair in 1585 survives. The bridge structure consists of six semi-circular stone arches with double arch rings, although one arch has been blocked leaving the bridge in the more attractive form of having an odd number of spans. The central span is nearly 13 ft. The bridge was widened on the north side in 1900 and a severe problem of subsidence was rectified in 1937. The cantilevered walkway was added in 1949.

In 1645 there was a three-day siege by one thousand Royalist troops of the Parliamentary forces holding the nearby castle, which resulted in skirmishes between the bridge and the castle, and various military artefacts from the time have been recovered from the river.

7. OLD BRIDGE, WOOL

It is known that a bridge crossed the River Frome on this site in 1343, but this one probably dates from Elizabethan times. The main structure consists of five nearly semicircular segmental stone arches, each with three wide ribs beneath, the largest arch spanning just over 15 ft. Each of the four river piers has large upstream and smaller downstream pointed cutwaters, all of which extend up to the low parapet level to form pedestrian refuges. At the south end there is an additional brick flood arch on a slightly different alignment which was built in the nineteenth century. This was the first bridge ordered to be repaired as a county bridge in 1742.

In *Tess of the d'Urbevilles* Thomas Hardy describes how Tess and Angel Clare cross the bridge to reach Wellbridge Manor for their ill-fated honeymoon. Local legend claims that the bridge is haunted by a ghostly coach with coachman and passengers and that the apparition has been seen many times - but only by those with Turbeville blood.

8. SMITH'S BRIDGE, BRADFORD ABBAS

Dating from the sixteenth century, this bridge over the River Yeo is one of the few Tudor four-centred arch bridges in Dorset. Built on a slight skew, it consists of two 13 ft spans with a central pier protected by pointed cutwaters. It is more usually referred to by the older inhabitants as 'Smear's Bridge'.

9. TOWN BRIDGE, STURMINSTER NEWTON

This bridge over the River Stour probably dates from the sixteenth century and consists of six pointed stone arches with the spans increasing towards the centre of the bridge. When the bridge was widened from its original 12 ft to 18 ft in 1820, further pointed

Opposite page top Old Bridge, Wool, with Woolbridge Manor on the right.
Opposite page bottom Smith's Bridge, Bradford Abbas.

Town Bridge, Sturminster Newton.

arches were constructed to span between the pointed cutwaters, and elegant corbelled refuges were built out over each side of the central pier. These make a pleasing focus to what would otherwise be the unresolved duality of an even number of spans on each side. The date of the reconstruction is recorded on a commemorative stone placed upside down on the south side of the central upstream cutwater, presumably so it can be read from above. When the County Council undertook repairs on the bridge in the early 1990s, the new work was painted with cow slurry to help it acquire a suitably aged appearance.

To the north of the bridge, flood relief is provided by a further structure, built in 1828, of six segmental and four semicircular stone arches spanning between piers with rounded cutwaters.

10. AXE BRIDGE, THORNCOMBE

This sixteenth century single track bridge not far from Forde Abbey is only 10 ft wide between parapets. It has three segmental stone arches, with spans varying between 9 ft and 11 ft over a paved invert. Interestingly, the central span is the smallest. The northern pier has pointed cutwaters on both sides, whereas the southern pier has a cutwater only on its eastern side, with the arch ring springing off a small corbel.

11. OUTER BRIDGE, CORFE CASTLE

The ravine which this bridge spans was cut by miners in 1207 to provide an additional defence for the castle and originally would have been spanned by a timber bridge with an opening section. The main structure as it now stands was built in the late sixteenth century, although the north abutment probably dates back a further three hundred years. The bridge consists of four unequal semicircular double ring stone arches standing on tall buttressed rectangular piers (For illustration see overleaf).

Outer Bridge, Corfe Castle.

12. STANBRIDGE MILL BRIDGE, HORTON

A bridge called 'Pons Petrae' crossing the River Allen on this site was first mentioned in 1279 as marking the outer limits of Cranborne Chase. However, the four pointed stone arches which form the oldest part of the existing structure probably date from much later; in particular the piers are unusually thin. The two central pointed arch spans are just under 7 ft wide. The bridge has subsequently been widened by about 2 ft on both sides, probably first in about 1760 to take the turnpike road from Ringwood to Shaftesbury, and further work was done in 1949. The segmental arches for the widened sections span about 8 ft.

Stanbridge Mill Bridge, Horton.

THE SEVENTEENTH CENTURY

The seventeenth century marked the gradual end of the Gothic style of building, exemplified by the pointed arch, and a continuing move towards lighter structures and greater bridge spans. The increasing size of the main span, even with segmental rather than semi-circular arches, tended to result in hump-backed bridges with steep approaches. In 1663 the first Turnpike Act was passed, with the intention of making all users rather than just local people pay for the upkeep of the country's roads and bridges. The general increase in trade during the century also led to the construction of most of the county's seven remaining packhorse bridges (17-19).

13. NORTH BRIDGE, WAREHAM

During the sixteenth century the bridge to the north of Wareham over the River Piddle was described as having six arches, and the earliest mention of North Bridge dates back to the fourteenth century. For many years, the parish of Moreton was responsible for half the cost of maintaining both the bridge and the causeway leading to it.

The present bridge, of three arches, may include part of that earlier medieval bridge but has been extensively rebuilt over the years. The northern arch spanning about 12 ft, which is pointed, is probably the oldest part still standing. The two other arches, which are of 15 ft span, are segmental, one being partially ribbed, and these probably date from about 1670. The bridge has been widened twice - in 1846 to 19 ft and again in the middle of the present century to 36 ft.

North Bridge, Wareham.

14. WALFORD BRIDGE, WIMBORNE

The seven arches of Walford Bridge cross the River Allen at the northern edge of Wimborne. The earlier seventeenth century structure, which can be seen on the west or upstream face of the bridge, has six pointed stone arches spanning nearly 10 ft between piers fronted by cutwaters. There is a single pedestrian refuge above the central pier. The seventh arch, at the northern end, is semicircular and was probably added during major remodelling of the bridge in 1802 to the design of William Evans. The bridge was widened on the downstream side in the nineteenth century with segmental stone arch rings spanning about 9 ft between extended piers and supporting brick spandrels. More recently, a concrete footway has been cantilevered out on this side.

15. JULIAN'S BRIDGE, WIMBORNE

Julian's Bridge, Wimborne, crossing the River Stour on the west of the town, was built in 1636 to replace an earlier bridge named after Walter Julien of Wimborne who lived during King John's reign. The bridge was repaired in 1713 and widened on both sides in 1844, when an additional arch was also constructed at the east end.

The bridge consists of the seven original narrow semicircular and pointed arches in stone and the later one in brick, with spans varying from 16 ft to 24 ft. When the bridge was widened to 18 ft between parapets, pointed brick arches with stone dressings were built over the cutwaters, framing the earlier spans. At the same time the parapets on both sides were enlivened by interesting little corbelled refuges over alternate piers. There are two stone cartouches on the downstream face of the central refuge, with the dates 1636 and 1844 commemorating the main events in the bridge's history.

In addition, there are three 9 ft flood arches at the west end, built in brick with stone dressings.

Opposite page top Walford Bridge, Wimborne.
Opposite page bottom Julian's Bridge, Wimborne.

The earliest written record of a bridge at Iford dates back to the twelfth century, although no trace of this structure remains. The existing old crossing over the River Stour is in three main parts. The eastern part, however, is for flood relief only and consists of four brick and two stone barrel arches, probably built in the late eighteenth century.

The central, oldest part of the bridge dates from the middle of the seventeenth century and consists of four semicircular stone arches spanning 12 ft between piers with pointed cutwaters. The roadway over this part is only 13 ft between parapets.

The first two arches of the western part, over the main channel, were built in 1784, following recommendations by Robert Mylne, designer of the original Blackfriars Bridge in London, who was then involved in a bridge being built over the Test at Romsey. These are segmental stone arches spanning 30 ft. In 1933, following the complete re-alignment of the road a short distance upstream, a further two matching arches were built at the eastern end of these eighteenth century spans, and all this section of the old road with its three bridges was limited to pedestrians only.

The new bridge over the river channel is built of engineering bricks and consists of three spans, a central semi-elliptical main span of 35 ft, and two semicircular side spans. In addition, there are six segmental and four semicircular brick flood arches.

17. PACKHORSE BRIDGE, RAMPISHAM

This remote little bridge, carrying an old track over a stream feeding the River Frome, probably dates from the early seventeenth century. It has two main stone arches, which are roughly four-centered, of about 7ft span and a smaller, probably later, arch at the north end. At over 5 ft wide between parapets, it is relatively wide for a packhorse bridge.

18. PACKHORSE BRIDGE, TARRANT MONKTON

The packhorse bridge over the River Tarrant at Tarrant Monkton, dating from about the seventeenth century, consists of three small segmental stone arches, the largest having a span of 6 ft and a rise of just under 2 ft. Like all packhorse bridges it was built just wide enough to give comfortable passage to a loaded beast, in this case 5 ft wide, but without any obstructing parapets. Modern timber railings have now been added and the appearance of the bridge has been further spoilt by the unsightly rendered coping and the brick retaining walls to the embankments behind the bridge abutments. However, the bridge's setting beside the watersplash is certainly picturesque when the water is flowing.

Above Packhorse Bridge, Tarrant Monkton.
Opposite page Packhorse Bridge, Rampisham.

19. PACKHORSE BRIDGE
FIFEHEAD NEVILLE

This interesting little 6 ft wide packhorse bridge crosses the River Divelish near the site of a Roman villa which was excavated in 1881 and 1902-05. The two 6 ft spans are unusual pointed triangular arches supported by a central pier with a cutwater on the upstream face. The bridge's age is uncertain, possibly dating back to medieval times, but it has been heavily restored over the years, with the timber railings added relatively recently.

THE EIGHTEENTH CENTURY

Early in the century, the turnpike system had passed out of its experimental stage and was becoming widely extended. Between 1700 and 1790 sixteen hundred Road Acts were passed, which resulted in the repair and improvement of many old bridges or the construction of new ones. In Dorset, for example, the ancient Stanbridge Mill Bridge at Horton (12) was widened about 1760 to take the turnpike.

The second half of the eighteenth century was also the start of the Canal Age, which lasted until about 1850 and resulted in the construction of many bridges. Although no canals were built in Dorset, the developing technology, particularly in the extensive use of brick in bridges, had its impact in the county. Witchampton Bridge (28), for example, is a handsome brick structure built in 1795. Other technical developments included the introduction of semi-elliptical arch spans, as at Beer Hackett (21), a good example of this style being the bridge built early in the following century at Marnhull (33).

The Canal Age led to the emergence of the civil engineer. At the same time, however, the eighteenth century was also the period when architects were designing grand classical bridges complete with balustrades and ornamentation, often as private commissions for wealthy landowners. Court Bridge, Frampton (23), reputedly by Christopher Wren, is an excellent Dorset example.

20. LONGHAM BRIDGE, HAMPRESTON

A few miles downstream from Wimborne, the River Stour is crossed by Longham Bridge. The bridge was first built in 1728 and rebuilt and widened in 1792. It has eleven segmental arches, a central span of 20 ft with side spans decreasing down to 15 ft. All but one span are of brick, spanning between stone piers. On the east face of the bridge is a footway cantilevered out on concrete beams, which was built in about 1960.

21. BEER HACKETT BRIDGE
BEER HACKETT

This otherwise insignificant little bridge was probably the first in Dorset to be given a semi-elliptical arch when the structure was rebuilt in the eighteenth century on earlier, possibly sixteenth century piers with pointed cutwaters. The bridge is built on a skew, with the 12 ft span main arch flanked by two semicircular side arches, the arches consisting of a single voussoir ring. Unfortunately, the cutwaters and arch barrels have now been rendered.

The Vineyard Bridge is almost right under the towering ramparts and walls of the slighted castle. It is a single eighteenth century nearly semicircular stone arch spanning about 18 ft and decorated with projecting keystones. The later parapets splay out at each end. Its nearness to the castle ruins means it probably uses stones which originally formed part of the ramparts.

The bridge owes its name to a house called The Vineyard, which was built at the end of the seventeenth century, or early in the eighteenth, close to the south west slope of Castle Hill.

23 . COURT BRIDGE, FRAMPTON

The bridge over the River Frome in Frampton Park is a little
eighteenth century gem and has been attributed to Christopher
Wren. Built privately in the classical style for the owners of
Frampton House, it consists of three segmental brick barrel arches
with ashlar facings and has a central span of 26 ft and flanking spans
of 21 ft. There is a small rounded cutwater at each end of the two
piers, capped with half domes, above which the spandrel wall is
decorated with a simple roundel. The road line is marked by a
projecting string course supporting an elegant balustrade which, at
the ends of the bridge, curves round to terminate in drum-shaped
pillars.

Pinford Bridge in Sherborne Park is another handsome eighteenth
century park bridge of three segmental arch spans, said to have been
built to the design of Robert Mylne in 1790, but is not open to the
public.

24. ROLLS MILL BRIDGE
STURMINSTER NEWTON

Records show that an earlier bridge at this site over the River Divelish and about half a mile north of Sturminster Newton was called either Rolles or Rawles Bridge. It was taken over by the county in 1635 and was ordered to be repaired in 1689. The present bridge lies about 10 feet to the west of a new bridge on a straightened

section of the Sherborne road. It has three segmental stone arches, the intermediate piers have rounded cutwaters both upstream and downstream with rounded tops, and the parapet walls have a rounded coping. The style is similar to many eighteenth century bridges in Wiltshire.

25. GREY'S BRIDGE, DORCHESTER

Grey's Bridge crosses the River Frome on the eastern edge of Dorchester a few hundred feet north of the site of the ancient Stockham or Stocking Bridge, which it replaced. It was built under Act of Parliament by the bounty of Mrs Lora Pitt (née Grey) of Kingston Maurward to avoid the dangerous route over the old bridge and was completed in 1748. The bridge consists of three moulded segmental stone arches, the central span being nearly 12 ft, flanked by outer spans of about 9 ft resulting in a hump-backed profile which is marked by the deep string course at the original road level. The piers have small pointed cutwaters. Over the abutments, which are noticeably wider than the bridge, the parapets step out at right angles to form spacious square pedestrian refuges. In 1927 the bridge was widened by 6 ft on the downstream face in reinforced concrete, with the original stonework to the elevation taken down and rebuilt.

This is the stone bridge, described in Hardy's *The Mayor of Casterbridge*, to which Michael Henchard came to ponder his fate and to learn that Farfrae had moved into his old home.

Above A detail from an eighteenth century engraving of Grey's Bridge.
Opposite page Grey's Bridge, Dorchester.

26. HIGHER WOOD BRIDGE
BISHOP'S CAUNDLE

Higher Wood Bridge over the River Caundle, which is considered to date from around 1770, has four semicircular stone arches spanning about 9 ft between tall narrow piers faced by tall rounded cutwaters. The bridge has been widened on both sides by the insertion of concrete cantilevers over the piers which, in turn, support a deep concrete edge beam capped by a stone coping.

27. BLANDFORD BRIDGE

This handsome bridge was largely built by William Moulton in 1783, although parts of the medieval ribbed arches from the earlier narrower bridge can still be seen under the span at the town end. The bridge was rebuilt and widened again, this time on the east side, by William Bushrod in 1812. It consists of six segmental stone arches, the central pair being slightly larger with spans of about 21 ft, all decorated with projecting keystones. The five piers have pointed cutwaters and the bridge parapet is unusually low.

28. WITCHAMPTON BRIDGE

The bridge at Witchampton over the River Allen, virtually unnoticeable to those passing over by car, is an attractive little structure when seen from the side. It was designed and built in classical style by the local builder Samuel Kent of Witchampton in 1795.

It consists of three segmental brick arches on stone piers, which step back above the foundations of an earlier bridge, and has cutwaters on the upstream face only. The central arch spans nearly 13 ft with a rise of about 5 ft, and the flanking arches span about 8 ft. The arch rings are 1½ bricks deep with stone keystones and an oversailing archivolt ring. There is a brick string course below the parapet which is topped with a stone coping and each abutment face features a blind brick roundel before the wing walls curve out to finish at right angles to the line of the bridge.

This bridge over the River Stour consists of three semicircular stone arches, the central one spanning about 26 ft and the two flanking arches 20 ft. The large triangular cutwaters are carried up to form much needed refuges on a busy, narrow crossing. It is possible that the bridge was built of stone from Eastbury House in Tarrant Gunville, which had been demolished a few years earlier.

A slate panel embedded at road level in the bridge's south parapet is inscribed 'The Bridge was Built by Hen. W. Portman Esq An. Dom. 1795 Joseph Towsey Architect'. It seems that Portman had disliked the coach road running through his estate and decided to close it. Accordingly he constructed the present highway which joined the Shaftesbury road just to the east of his new bridge. The Portman family later built the nearby Bryanston House on the estate.

THE VICTORIAN AGE

Early in the century there were over 20,000 miles of good turnpike roads in England. Traditional stone road bridge building continued, although cutwaters, for example, were now generally rounded not pointed, as at Canford Bridge, Wimborne (32), built in 1813. Arches, too, became much flatter, as at Fitches Bridge, Pamphill (36) and bridge builders began to use iron as a structural material, cast iron girders and wrought iron ties being used in Bagber Bridge (34), built in 1830. In 1825 though, the first public railway opened and by about 1840 nearly every turnpike trust was bankrupt, the cost of keeping the roads and bridges in repair falling onto the local ratepayers. The 1874 List of County Bridges shows that by then the County of Dorset had taken responsibility for 93 bridges which were newly built or had previously belonged to the turnpike trusts.

The railways brought phenomenal changes and, in the three decades between 1830 and 1860, resulted in the number of all the bridges in the country doubling to about 50,000. This huge upsurge in bridge building activity led to rapid introduction of new materials and technology and the emergence of the engineer as hero. The impact of the railways is exemplified by Frampton Viaduct (38), designed by the famous Isambard Kingdom Brunel, and the great brick viaducts at Poole (40) that stride magnificently and contemptuously over valleys and dwellings.

Lower Bockhampton Bridge, Stinsford.

30. LOWER BOCKHAMPTON BRIDGE, STINSFORD

This, the most northern of a series of brick arch bridges over the River Frome at Kingston Maurward, was probably built in the early nineteenth century. It is a triple arched hump-backed segmental bridge in mellow brickwork, but with keystones and piers in Portland stone. The central arch is of 14 ft span with side spans of 10 ft. The parapets, which are topped by a rounded brick coping, curve out gracefully at the ends.

31. FROME BRIDGE, TINCLETON

The White Mead tributary of the River Frome is crossed just south of Tincleton by this early nineteenth century bridge. It consists of three flat segmental brick arches spanning about 12 ft between brick piers with pointed cutwaters. The abutments are decorated with brick pilasters before the wing walls curve away to end parallel to the river. An unusually deep stone coping caps the brick parapet.

The grassy roadside verges continue over the bridge and, with the absence of much traffic, suggests a scene straight out of the 1920s.

Frome Bridge, Tincleton.

32. CANFORD BRIDGE, WIMBORNE

The Canford Bridge over the Stour on the road south from Wimborne to Poole was completed in 1813, as recorded on the inscription on the north pier under the middle arch: 'This BRIDGE finished in the Year 1813 by JOHN DYSON, Engineer [and] JESSE BUSHROD, Mason'. It is a handsome structure of three stone arches, a central one of 40 ft span being flanked on each side by slightly smaller spans of about 34 ft, thus giving a pleasing vertical curve to the overall elevation.

Both river piers have cutwaters which taper off into the middle of the spandrel wall about halfway between the springing and coping levels. The voussoir stones have been dressed to form a distinct archivolt ring, although this is partly damaged. On the east, downstream face there is an oversailing string course at road level below the stone parapet. On the west face a modern concrete cantilever footpath has been built outside the parapet on the line of this string course. Just south of the bridge there are a further six smaller flood arches each consisting of a single brick ring and brick spandrels.

The contract papers in the County Record Office in Dorchester show that Bushrod was forced to ask for additional payment to cover the extra costs caused by a ten week strike by the quarrymen of Portland.

33. KING'S MILL BRIDGE, MARNHULL

This bridge over the River Stour was designed in 1823 by G. A. Underwood to replace an earlier bridge which dated from 1673. It is probably on the site of a much earlier bridge which in 1358 was reported as 'weak, by default of the Abbott of Glastonbury'.

The bridge has three semi-elliptical brick barrelled arches, the central one spanning about 25 ft, with stone voussoirs on the faces. The intermediate heavy stone piers have half-octagonal cutwaters and the bridge is decorated with stone roundels in the centre of the spandrels over the piers. The parapets, which are also embellished with stone panels, are set back at the abutments.

Canford Bridge, Wimborne.

King's Mill Bridge, Marnhull.

Bagber Bridge over the River Lydden was designed by W. Dawes and built in 1830. It consists of four cast iron girders, 23" deep and 14½" wide, spanning 33 ft at 5 ft centres and supporting a modern concrete deck. Beneath each girder are two 1½" diameter wrought iron rods. When the bridge was built these would have been tensioned to give a prestress to the bridge, although it is doubtful if any significant tension still remains in the rods.

35 . HURST SOUTH BRIDGE, MORETON

The South Bridge at Hurst, designed by William Evans, is the largest of three bridges built in 1834 as part of a causeway over the water meadows of the River Frome. It was funded by public subscription following an initial anonymous donation of £500.

The bridge has eight segmental brick arches in two groups of four divided by a central brick pier with pointed cutwaters which extend up to form pedestrian refuges on each side. The other, smaller, intermediate brick piers have rounded stone cutwaters which are capped with rounded tops. The wing walls to the abutments splay out to end in small brick piers. A stone coping surmounts the low brick parapet.

36. FITCHES BRIDGE, PAMPHILL

Fitches Bridge over the River Allen was built in 1841 and has a flat 20 ft segmental arch span with a rise of only about 2 ft 9 in. The arch consists of a single brick ring of stretcher and header bricks supporting a brick spandrel through which five tie rods have been placed to prevent it bowing. Immediately behind the springing points there is a brick pilaster before the wing walls of the abutment curve gracefully out over stepped back foundations, finishing in square piers. The brick parapet is supported on an oversailing string course of brick headers. Unfortunately, however, overgrowing vegetation rather spoils the overall effect of this charming little bridge.

In 1959 the foundations were at risk of being undermined but 90 tons of stone was placed to protect the paved invert and save the bridge.

37. LONGFORD BRIDGE, THORNFORD

This handsome flat segmental stone arch bridge over the River Wriggle has a span of 36 ft and a rise of only just over 5 ft. It probably dates from around the middle of the nineteenth century.

38. FRAMPTON VIADUCT,
SYDLING ST NICHOLAS

The Wiltshire, Somerset and Weymouth Railway was promoted and funded by the G.W.R. as a means of keeping the London & South Westerly Railway out of the west of England. The central 24 ft span of this impressive masonry structure carries the line from Dorchester to Yeovil over a minor country road, with Sydling Water running about 6 ft below road level through the western arch. The brick piers are lightened by four tall arched cross openings 4 ft wide. The massive scale of the details is exemplified by the heavy string course at track level.

The bridge, which was designed by the great Victorian engineer Isambard Kingdom Brunel, who was chief engineer of the G.W.R., was completed in 1857.

39. RAILWAY VIADUCT, CORFE CASTLE

This bridge was built in 1885 to take the single track Wareham to Swanage Railway on a curved alignment over the River Corfe just to the east of the great castle. It consists of four 28 ft semicircular arches supported by square piers with shallow buttresses. The

railway was closed in 1972 but, since 1984, is being re-opened in
stages. The bridge is a distinctive landmark in an area of outstanding
natural beauty and acts as a Victorian foil to the romantic grandeur
of the medieval castle ruins.

40. BOURNE VALLEY RAILWAY VIADUCT, POOLE

This viaduct is one of a pair of handsome brick viaducts and was completed in 1885 to carry the tracks across the Bourne Valley for the London and South Western Railway's direct link between Bournemouth and Poole, although the line itself was not opened until 1888. The eastern viaduct, which led to Bournemouth West station, is no longer used.

The viaduct, which rises slightly from north to south, has ten spans, mostly 28 ft wide but including two wider 33 ft span road crossings. These are built on the skew between larger piers decorated with brick pilasters with stone dressings. The arches themselves consist of five brick rings, the outer one projecting, with recessed brick panels containing a triangular stone feature enlivening each spandrel.

The viaduct still bears the scars of the damage caused by the air raid of 27th March 1941 on the neighbouring Branksome Gas Works, when 34 people were killed.

41. SUSPENSION BRIDGE, CANFORD MAGNA

This pedestrian footbridge, built towards the end of the century, spans 132 ft over the River Stour and is mentioned in the delightful book *Six Men on the Stour*, an account of a boating holiday in 1892. The two steel cables, which are hung between cast iron pillars and anchored in large concrete blocks, support lattice girders each side which in turn support the 2 ft wide deck. These girders, which also act as railings for pedestrians, help to stiffen the bridge against vertical displacement caused by the weight of people crossing, and horizontal stiffening is provided by further cables stretched between extensions of the deck supports and the river banks.

THE TWENTIETH CENTURY

Following the earlier Canal and Railway Ages, this century has been the Age of the Motor Vehicle. The huge growth in road traffic has led to old bridges being widened or replaced, as at Wareham's North Bridge (13) or its South Bridge (44), and new bridges being constructed to bypass villages and towns, as at Wimborne (49).

New materials have been introduced, such as reinforced concrete, as at Tuckton Bridge, Bournemouth (43) in 1905 and prestressed concrete, as at Braidley Road Bridge, Bournemouth (48) in 1970. Design concepts have developed too and it is hoped that the start of the next century will be marked by construction of the country's first multi-span cable-stayed bridge over Holes Bay in Poole Harbour. The winning design from 99 entries in the international competition for a new bridge was for a delicate cable-stayed structure which, the designers say, will 'tiptoe across the bay'.

An artist's impression of the projected new bridge over Holes Bay, Poole.
(Design: Flint & Neill Partnership, Dissing & Weitling, Rambøll, Terence O'Rourke. Image: Nick Wood/Hayes Davidson.)

42. ALUM CHINE SUSPENSION BRIDGE, BOURNEMOUTH

The 10 ft wide footbridge which crosses Alum Chine may have been intended originally for horse-drawn carriages. It now forms part of an easy cliff top walk from Bournemouth Pier to Branksome and Poole. The bridge is of the suspension type and was completed in 1904. It consists of two pairs of $1^{3}/_{4}$" diameter steel cables spanning 230 ft between small steel framed towers encased in concrete. Thirty one hangers are clamped at equal intervals to each pair of cables to support a lattice girder on each side of the bridge. These girders in turn support and stiffen the deck structure as well as providing the necessary safety fencing for pedestrians.

The bridge was extensively repaired in 1973 when the main cables and the timber deck were renewed and other corroded components replaced.

Tuckton Bridge, Bournemouth.

Despite popular myth, it was not from this bridge, which had not then been built, but from a smaller rustic bridge in the neighbouring Branksome Dene Chine, that Winston Churchill fell 29 feet in 1893.

43. TUCKTON BRIDGE, BOURNEMOUTH

The Tuckton Bridge Company, founded by Dr Thomas Compton of Southbourne, built the first Tuckton Bridge over the Stour in timber, and this was opened as a toll bridge in 1883. In 1904 Bournemouth Council purchased the bridge for £15,000 and the following year completed a new bridge to enable the Bournemouth tramway system to extend through to Christchurch. This was one of the first re-inforced concrete bridges to be built in the country. It has 14 spans with a central span of 41 ft. Each span consists of three parallel arch ribs, cast to form a segment of a circle with a rise of 5 ft, which support the deck structure on short square columns. The piers are supported on reinforced concrete piles driven into the river bed. The bridge remained a toll bridge until tolls were finally abolished in 1943.

44. SOUTH BRIDGE, WAREHAM

The present bridge over the Frome at Wareham is the third or fourth to exist on the site. John Leland described seeing a Norman-style bridge of six ribbed arches but a century later, in 1649, the bridge was in such a condition that there was a petition from the poor inhabitants of the town to 'pray that the repairs may be done by the County.' In the later editions of Hutchins it was reported that the bridge, then of seven arches, had been ordered to be replaced in 1775 and that a handsome bridge of five arches of Portland stone had been completed in 1779 at a total cost of £2932.10.0.

The modern bridge was built in 1924-1927, the eastern half being built first while the old bridge continued in use after which the latter was demolished. Strenuous efforts were made to save the old bridge, including reminding the County Surveyor of the bridge plates warning of the dire penalty of transportation for life for anyone 'injuring' the bridge, but to no avail. Some of the stones were saved and used in extensions to nearby Trigon House. During the construction work an eleventh century sword was found in the river.

The bridge consists of three low-rise reinforced concrete arches, with the arch ring standing out from the plane of the spandrels. The earlier style of bridge is further replicated by the cutwaters above the piers which continue through to parapet level to provide small viewing points off the pavements. The concrete parapet wall has a large and distinctive central upstand. The main span is 58 ft and the two outer spans are each 36 ft long.

45. TOWN BRIDGE, WEYMOUTH

This bridge, which was built in 1930, is the fifth bridge to have been built on the site and is very similar to the lifting bridge in Poole, which was completed in 1927. It is a double leaf rolling bascule, in which the rear of the girder at the side of each lifting arm is constructed to form a circular toothed quadrant which rotates along horizontal racks. Thus, as the lifting arms rise into the air, they also move back to leave a clear navigable opening of 76 ft.

South Bridge, Wareham.

Town Bridge, Weymouth.

46. TWOFORDS BRIDGE, LYDLINCH

The original bridge across the River Lydden at this point was probably built in the 1830s. It had two segmental arches separated by semicircular cutwaters with rounded tops. During the Second World War it was considered to be too weak to take the heavy military vehicles likely to head south to the ports of Weymouth and Portland when a Second Front was finally opened in Europe. In 1942 Canadian Army engineers therefore erected a new Callendar-Hamilton galvanised steel lattice girder bridge, which is similar to but rather heavier than the more familiar Bailey bridge. This bridge, which carries the eastbound traffic over the river, was recently strengthened to take 40 ton lorries. A recently erected commemorative plaque on the bridge reads 'D-Day 6th June. 50th Anniversary 1944-1994. Dorset County Council.'

47. FORD FOOTBRIDGE, MORETON

This six span footbridge was built in 1950 over the River Frome alóngside the picturesque ford at Moreton. It consists of two parallel prestressed concrete beams with infill slabs spanning between simple concrete piers at 34 ft centres. Although, like so many precast concrete structures, the bridge lacks intrinsic grace, the contrast between its straight lines and the over-arching trees makes a pleasing picture.

48. BRAIDLEY ROAD BRIDGE BOURNEMOUTH

This prestressed concrete bridge was opened in 1970 as part of a new town centre by-pass to relieve severe traffic congestion in the middle of Bournemouth. It crosses a small valley with two central spans of 140 ft flanked by two outer spans of 100 ft, the three intermediate supports being slender V-shaped concrete piers. The deck structure is made up of a series of longitudinal hollow concrete boxes through which pass some 140 high tensile steel cables. After the whole bridge had been constructed on temporary scaffolding, these cables were tightened up using 70 ton jacks, the resulting prestress allowing the bridge to support itself and a full load of vehicles. Braidley Road Bridge was the first bridge in the UK to be built with the internal tensioning cables not encased in concrete, although the original cables themselves subsequently had to be replaced because of corrosion.

The bridge's innovative design, by the consulting engineers E.W.H. Gifford & Partners, and the high quality of the contractor's finished concrete work have twice been recognised by the Concrete Society. The bridge received a Judges' Mention in the Society's 1970 Awards and a Commendation in the Mature Structures category in 1994.

49. RIVER STOUR BRIDGE, WIMBORNE

This bridge was constructed as part of the A31 Wimborne by-pass and completed in 1981. The structure, consisting of five longitudinal continuous steel plate girders, has three spans - a central main span of 34 metres between piers located on the river banks, and 18 metre side spans. The underside of the girders is shaped to a gently curving profile which, with the bridge's low height and slender proportions, gives it an elegant elevation.

Opposite page top Braidley Road Bridge, Bournemouth.
Opposite page bottom The bridge carrying the Wimborne by-pass over the River Stour.

50. ST GEORGE'S VIADUCT, DORCHESTER

This bridge, completed in 1988, carries the Dorchester bypass over the River Frome. It has five main spans of 23.0 metres and two end spans 21.5 metres long. The intermediate supports each consist of twin concrete piers with clearly exposed pier-top bearings supporting a cross head beam. This in turn supports four continuous longitudinal rolled steel joists and a composite concrete deck slab. The clean, modern lines give the bridge an attractive appearance.

GLOSSARY

ABUTMENT. The support at the end of either a single span bridge or a series of bridge spans. See also pier.

ARCH. A curved structural member which supports loads by resistance to axial compression along its length. The shape of the arch in a bridge gives its distinctive character. The most common bridge arch shapes are semi-circular, pointed, segmental and semi-elliptical. Arches exert a lateral thrust against their abutments, this thrust increasing as the arch becomes flatter. In multi-arch bridges, the thrust from one arch is counterbalanced by the massiveness of the intermediate piers or by the thrust from the neighbouring arch.

ARCHIVOLT. The projecting stone edging to an arch ring.

ASHLAR. Smoothly dressed blocks of approximately square-faced stone-work laid with very thin joints.

BASCULE BRIDGE. A type of drawbridge in which the opening span pivots on a horizontal axis and is balanced by a counterweight (from the French *bascule* meaning see-saw).

CABLE STAY. A structure in which the intermediate supports to a con-tinuous beam are not from piers beneath the beam but from diagonal ties, made from high strength steel cable, stretching above the point of support to a main pier or pylon which extends to some distance above the beam.

CANTILEVER. A beam which is firmly fixed at one end and unsupported at the other in the manner of a bracket.

CENTERING. The temporary structure, usually made of timber, on which an arch is constructed.

CONTINUOUS BEAM. A rigid beam spanning between three or more con-secutive supports without any structural break, thus giving it greater strength than comparably sized beams spanning the openings singly.

CORBEL. A projection from a wall which supports a beam, arch, parapet or statue.

CUTWATER. A pointed or rounded upstream and (sometimes) downstream extension to a bridge pier at water level to smooth the flow of water past the pier.

KEYSTONE. The central stone in a ring of voussoirs forming an arch. Structurally, the keystone is no more important than any other stone in an arch ring (as with the links in a chain) but, being at the crown of the arch and the last to be laid, is sometimes made visually more dominant.

PIER. The intermediate support between two spans of a bridge. See also abutment.

POINTED ARCH. An arch in which the curves on each side meet at the apex without this representing a common tangent point.

PRESTRESSED CONCRETE. Concrete in which high strength steel cables, set to a precise profile and buried in the concrete, are tightened up after the concrete has hardened (post-tensioned) in order to counteract the tensile stresses induced from the self weight of the bridge and its expected load of vehicles and people.

RIB. The part of a masonry arch which projects beneath the main barrel of the arch and was usually constructed first to economise on centering, the remaining part of the barrel being constructed by spanning stones between adjacent ribs.

RISE (of an arch). The vertical distance between a horizontal line joining the springing points of an arch and the underside of its highest point.

SEGMENTAL ARCH. An arch formed from an arc of a circle smaller than a semicircle.

SEMI-ELLIPTICAL ARCH. An arch in which the shape is a curve joining points located a constant distance from two fixed points called foci. In a semi-elliptical stone arch every voussoir in each half arch has to be cut individually and precisely.

SKEW. The obliqueness between the centreline of a bridge and a line at right angles to the abutment face.

SPANDREL. The roughly triangular-shaped vertical area between the outside of an arch ring and the underside of the bridge deck structure.

SPRINGING. The point at which the curved underside of an arch meets the face of a pier or abutment.

SUSPENSION BRIDGE. A bridge in which the deck is supported by hangers from a number of cables that are suspended between tall towers and anchored firmly into the ground at each end.

VOUSSOIR. A wedge-shaped member of accurately dressed masonry which, with its neighbours, makes up the structural part of an arch. For semicircular or segmental arches the voussoirs can be interchangeable; with semi-elliptical arches, every voussoir in each half arch must be individually shaped.

FURTHER READING

Casson, Sir Hugh, *Bridges*, Chatto and Windus for the National Benzole Company, 1963

Hinchliffe, Ernest, *A Guide to the Packhorse Bridges of England*, Cicerone Press, 1994

Hutchings, Monica, *Dorset River*, Macdonald & Co., 1956

Jervoise, E., *The Ancient Bridges of the South of England*, Architectural Press, 1930

Johnson, S. M., & Scott-Giles, C. W. (eds), *British Bridges: An Illustrated and Historical Record*, The Public Works, Roads & Transport Congress, 1933

Maré, Eric de, *The Bridges of Britain*, Batsford, 1954

Otter, R. A., *Civil Engineering Heritage: Southern England*, Thomas Telford, 1994

Poole Harbour Crossing, Emap Construct, 1997

Richards, J. M., *The National Trust Book of Bridges*, Jonathan Cape, 1984

Royal Commission on Historical Monuments England, *An Inventory of the Historical Monuments in the County of Dorset*, HMSO, 1952, 1970, 1972, 1975

Samuel, Olive J., *On the Bridge - A History of Town Bridge, Christchurch*, Olive J. Samuel, 1991

Stanier, Peter, *Dorset's Industrial Heritage*, Twelveheads Press, 1989

Wallis, A. J., *Dorset Bridges: A History and Guide*, Abbey Press Sherborne, 1974

Young, J. A., *Iford Bridge*, Bournemouth Local Studies Publications, 1978

ACKNOWLEDGEMENTS

We would like to acknowledge the help we have received from Dorset County Council, as well as from librarians and all those who have allowed us access to their land to study the bridges at close quarters and take photographs. We would like to thank Christopher Chaplin for drawing the map.

The

DISCOVER DORSET

Series of Books

A series of paperback books providing informative illustrated
introductions to Dorset's history, culture and way of life.
The following titles have so far been published.

BRIDGES *David McFetrich and Jo Parsons*

CASTLES AND FORTS *Colin Pomeroy*

CRANBORNE CHASE *Desmond Hawkins*

GEOLOGY *Paul Ensom*

THE GEORGIANS *Jo Draper*

THE INDUSTRIAL PAST *Peter Stanier*

ISLE OF PURBECK *Paul Hyland*

LEGENDS *Jeremy Harte*

PORTLAND *Stuart Morris*

POTTERY *Penny Copland-Griffiths*

THE PREHISTORIC AGE *Bill Putnam*

SAXONS AND VIKINGS *David Hinton*

SHIPWRECKS *Maureen Attwooll*

STONE QUARRYING *Jo Thomas*

THE VICTORIANS *Jude James*

All the books about Dorset published by The Dovecote Press
are available in bookshops throughout the county,
or in case of difficulty direct from the publishers.
The Dovecote Press Ltd, Stanbridge,
Wimborne, Dorset BH21 4JD
Tel: 01258 840549.